# Franz Schubert
## Symphony No. 7 in B minor / h Moll
### D 759 'Unfinished' / „Unvollendete"

Edited by / Herausgegeben von
Teresa Reichenberger

Urtext

T0081232

EULENBURG

EAS 129
ISBN 978-3-7957-6529-3
ISMN M-2002-2352-1

© 2007 Ernst Eulenburg & Co GmbH, Mainz
for Europe excluding the British Isles
Ernst Eulenburg Ltd, London
for all other countries
Urtext edition based on Eulenburg Study Score ETP 403
CD ℗ 1989 & © 1991 Naxos Rights International Ltd

Ernst Eulenburg Ltd
48 Great Marlborough Street
London W1F 7BB

# Contents / Inhalt

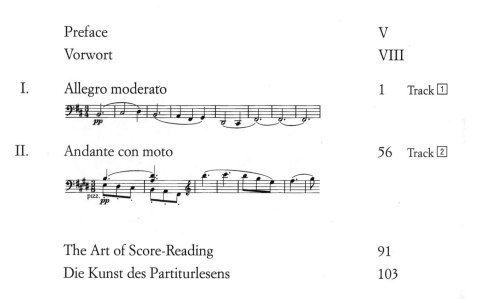

# Preface

**Composed: 1822**
**First performance: 17 December 1865, Redoutensaal, Vienna;**
**conducted by Johann Herbeck**
**First publication: C. A. Spina, Vienna, 1867**
**Instrumentation: 2 Flutes, 2 Oboes, 2 Clarinets, 2 Bassoons –**
**2 Horns, 2 Trumpets, 3 Trombones – Timpani – Strings**
**Duration: ca. 26 minutes**

On the title-page of the autograph, Schubert gave the starting date for the manuscript score of his Symphony in B minor as 30 October 1822. Sketches for it must date from the same month, following completion of the Mass in A flat major (September 1822).

The origin of the work, its subsequent fate and the circumstances of its incompleteness remain obscure and for over a century have given rise to numerous speculations. The works closest chronologically to the Symphony, such as songs (e.g. 'Die Liebe hat gelogen' D 751, *Nachtviolen* D 752, *Heliopolis* I/II, D 753/4), the Mass in A flat major, or the Fantasy in C major for piano ('Wanderer' Fantasy), for which Schubert had put the Symphony to one side in November 1822, provide no clues to the character or format of this symphony. It is even less easy to categorize the work within Schubert's symphonic output: earlier came six completed symphonies, whose composition fell, without any significant break, between the years 1813 and 1818, and sketches for two symphonies, in D major (1818) and E major (1821), which remain in draft form.

The time span between Schubert's early symphonies and the B minor Symphony also implies a stylistic change. While the above-mentioned works still conform to the classical symphonic style and can be placed within the Mozartian tradition, the B minor Symphony, with its anticipation of 'romantic feeling' and its superiority over all previous compositions in terms of content and conception, initiates Schubert's series of great instrumental works. Schubert's comment that he wanted to 'pave the way towards the great symphony' relates to this development, which culminates in his last symphony, the 'Great C major'.

Besides the two complete movements, *Allegro moderato* in B minor and *Andante con moto* in E major, Schubert left 20 bars of a Scherzo in B minor, headed *Allegro*, which is only orchestrated up to the ninth bar. It was in this state that the score came into the hands of Josef Hüttenbrenner, Schubert's close friend and pupil, in 1823. The former was supposed to take the score to Graz to his brother Anselm (well known to Schubert from his student years in

Vienna), probably in connection with the conferring on Schubert of honorary membership of the Steiermärkische Musikverein, with whom Anselm Hüttenbrenner was involved. It is not known when Hüttenbrenner actually came into possession of the Symphony. As he made no date for a performance of the symphonic fragment, the work disappeared from public view for the next decades. All we know is that Hüttenbrenner arranged the two movements for piano duet. It was not until 1865 that Johann Herbeck (1831–77), Court Kapellmeister and artistic director of the Gesellschaft der Musikfreunde in Vienna, came into possession of the safely preserved manuscript while visiting Hüttenbrenner in Graz. On the 17 December 1865 the first performance took place, conducted by Herbeck, in the large Redoutensaal of the Vienna Hofburg. Later the Viennese patron of the arts Nikolaus Dumba acquired the score of the Symphony in B minor, and the piano sketches belonging to it. After his death both came into the possession of the Gesellschaft der Musikfreunde.

In 1867 the score and parts were published for the first time by the Viennese publisher C. A. Spina with the title 'Two movements of the Unfinished Symphony in B minor'.

The fact of its incompleteness has always surrounded the Symphony with an aura of mystery, although Schubert did leave several other fragments – the unfinished string quartet in C minor of 1820, known as the 'Quartett-Satz', for example. No unfinished composition has occupied musicians and musicologists so intently as this particular Symphony. The possibility that Schubert did in fact complete the four movements and that the missing movements had been lost was dismissed by Christa Landon's discovery of the missing five pages of the autograph score, on one page of which the instrumentation broke off while the remaining four were empty. Countless attempts at completing the score retrospectively are based on this theory – among them that of Gerald Abraham who added an entr'acte from the play *Rosamunde*. A further theory claims that it was self-criticism that caused Schubert to give up work in the middle of the Scherzo, which he felt to be substandard. Maurice J. E. Brown relates the composition to Schubert's tragic illness, syphilis, at the end of 1822, which prevented him for psychological reasons from taking up work again on the composition. Consideration of Schubert's compositional method is of great significance, and this is fully apparent in the preserved drafts. In the Symphony in B minor, as in many other cases, the piano sketches contain the entire conception of the subsequent orchestral score, which is essentially simply a neat copy. For whatever reasons Schubert broke off in the third movement, it would have contradicted his usual method of work to have made alterations retrospectively, or to have taken up the work anew.

In the field of symphonic music Schubert never achieved the breakthrough that he did with his songs from the beginning of the 1820s – typical products of the Biedermeier period. Contemporary concert programmes and advertisements indicate an intense cultivation of Schubert's vocal composition. There was no lack of admiration or patronage either, as is clear from the organisation of so-called 'Schubertiades', i.e. house concerts among the circle of followers, and 'dedicatory compositions'. Perhaps most worthy of credit among Schubert's friends of those years was the Viennese lawyer Leopold Sonnleithner (1797–1873), who together with several art-lovers financed the first edition of a Schubert song ('Erlkönig'). A further 12 volumes were financed by him personally and sold on commission by the publishing house

Cappi & Diabelli. During the next two years Schubert's name became increasingly familiar in Vienna, especially through the performance of two *Singspiele* in leading Viennese theatres.

In contrast to his great model, Beethoven, who, in his own lifetime, was already celebrated as the master of symphonic writing, Schubert first won renown as a composer of Lieder and as a master of chamber music forms. Nevertheless, in the field of symphonic writing too, he succeeded with the B minor Symphony in breaking away for the first time from his earlier models, achieving a completely autonomous masterpiece. The year in which it was composed, 1822, is thus 'the mark of his full maturity as a composer'.

Unlike the formalistic compositional method of the Viennese classicists, Schubert's was based on the principle of change. Musical events are borne predominantly by the melody which, at its first appearance, is already self-contained and song-like, as for example the two themes of the first movement of the B minor Symphony (wind theme bars 13–20, string theme bars 44–53). Neither of these themes, however provides material for the development, which is concerned only with the theme of the introduction (bars 1–8). The slow second movement is made up of two parts which are both repeated in the manner of a recapitulation.

The pre-eminence of this work – and not only within Schubert's symphonic output – can be attributed to the wonderful melodic ideas, the characteristic tone colour and the richness of the harmony, achieved through modulation to distant keys, sudden changes from major to minor and enharmonic modulation.

Without going into the misunderstandings concerning the numbering of Schubert's last symphonies, it should nevertheless be mentioned that the incorrect numbering of the B minor as No.8 and the Great as No.7 dates back to Johannes Brahms and the old complete edition. In order to re-establish the chronological order the C major Symphony frequently is tagged as No.9. Since the revised edition of 'Deutsch' numbers in German the 'Unfinished' appears in the chronologically correct position of No.7.

Teresa Reichenberger
Translation: Penelope Souster

# Vorwort

**Komponiert:** 1822
**Uraufführung:** 17. Dezember 1865, Redoutensaal, Wien;
**Dirigent:** Johann Herbeck
**Erstveröffentlichung:** C. A. Spina, Wien, 1867
**Orchesterbesetzung:** 2 Flöten, 2 Oboen, 2 Klarinetten, 2 Fagotte –
2 Hörner, 2 Trompeten, 3 Posaunen – Pauken – Streicher
**Spieldauer:** etwa 26 Minuten

Schubert datierte den Beginn der Partiturniederschrift seiner Sinfonie in h-Moll auf dem Titelblatt des Autographs mit dem 30. Oktober 1822. Skizzen hierzu dürften in demselben Monat entstanden sein, im Anschluss an die Vollendung der Messe in As-Dur (September 1822).

Die Entstehung des Werkes und dessen späteres Schicksal liegen ebenso wie der Umstand des Fragmentarischen im Verborgenen und geben seit einem Jahrhundert Anlass zu vielerlei Vermutungen. Denn die in unmittelbarer zeitlicher Nachbarschaft entstandenen Werke, wie Lieder (z. B. „Die Liebe hat gelogen" D 751, *Nachtviolen* D 752, *Heliopolis* I/II, D 753/4), die Messe in As-Dur oder die Fantasie in C-Dur für Klavier („Wandererfantasie"), für welche Schubert die Sinfonie im November 1822 beiseite gelegt hat, bieten keinen Zugang zu Charakter und Format der vorliegenden Sinfonie. Noch weniger lässt sich das Werk innerhalb Schuberts sinfonischem Schaffen einordnen: vorangegangen waren sechs vollendete Sinfonien, deren Entstehung ohne größerer Unterbrechung in die Jahre 1813 bis 1818 fiel, und zwei Sinfonieskizzen in D-Dur (1818) und E-Dur (1821), die Versuche blieben.

Der zeitliche Abstand der h-Moll-Sinfonie zu Schuberts frühen Sinfonien impliziert gleichzeitig eine stilistische Wende. Während die genannten Werke noch dem klassischen Sinfoniestil zuzuordnen und an der Mozart-Tradition orientiert sind, eröffnet die h-Moll-Sinfonie mit ihrer Vorwegnahme des „romantischen Lebensgefühls" und ihrer Überlegenheit an Gehalt und Anlage allem bisher Geschaffenen die Reihe von Schuberts großen Instrumentalwerken. Zweifellos bezieht sich die Bemerkung Schuberts, er wolle sich „den Weg zur großen Sinfonie bahnen", auf diese Entwicklung, an deren Spitze seine letzte Sinfonie, die „Große C-Dur" von 1825, steht.

Schubert hinterließ neben den ersten beiden vollständigen Sätzen *Allegro moderato* in h-Moll und *Andante con moto* in E-Dur zwanzig Takte eines *Allegro* überschriebenen Scherzos in h-Moll, welches nur bis zum neunten Takt voll instrumentiert ist. In diesem Zustand geriet die Partitur im Jahre 1823 in die Hände von Josef Hüttenbrenner, Schuberts engem Freund und Schüler. Jener sollte die Partitur seinem Bruder Anselm, Schubert aus dessen Wiener Studienjahren gut bekannt, nach Graz überbringen, vermutlich im Zusammenhang mit der Ernennung Schuberts zum Ehrenmitglied des Steiermärkischen Musikvereins, bei dem auch Anselm Hüttenbrenner tätig war. Es ist nicht bekannt, wann Hüttenbrenner in den Besitz der Sinfonie gelangte. Da er keine Anstalten zu einer Aufführung des Sinfonie-Torsos machte, verschwand das Werk für die nächsten Jahrzehnte aus dem Blickfeld der Öffentlichkeit. Wir wissen nur, dass Hüttenbrenner die beiden Sätze für Klavier vierhändig gesetzt hat. Erst im Jahr 1865 erhielt Johann Herbeck (1831–1877), Hofkapellmeister und artistischer Direktor der Gesellschaft der Musikfreunde in Wien, das gut aufbewahrte Manuskript, als er Hütten-brenner in Graz aufsuchte. Am 17. Dezember 1865 fand unter Herbecks Leitung im großen Redoutensaal der Wiener Hofburg die erste Aufführung statt. Die Partitur der h-Moll-Sinfonie erwarb später der Wiener Kunstmäzen Nikolaus Dumba (1830–1900), ebenso die dazugehörigen Klavierskizzen. Beides ging nach seinem Tod an die Gesellschaft der Musik-freunde über.

Im Jahre 1867 erschienen Partitur und Stimmen mit dem Titel „Zwei Sätze der unvollendeten Sinfonie in H moll" beim Wiener Verlag C. A. Spina erstmals im Druck.

Der unvollendete Zustand umgab die Sinfonie seit jeher mit dem Nimbus des Geheimnisvol-len, obgleich Schubert nicht wenige Fragmente hinterlassen hat, wie z. B. das nicht zu Ende komponierte und als „Quartett-Satz" bekannte Streichquartett in c-Moll von 1820. Keine unvollendet gebliebene Komposition hat Musiker und Musikwissenschaftler so intensiv beschäftigt wie die vorliegende. Die Vermutung, Schubert hätte das viersätzig konzipierte Werk vollendet und die fehlenden Sätze wären verloren gegangen, wurde spätestens durch Christa Landons Entdeckung der fehlenden fünf Seiten des Partiturautographs, davon eine Seite, auf der die Instrumentation abbricht und vier leere, entkräftet. Auf dieser Theorie basieren zahlreiche Versuche, die Sinfonie nachträglich zu vervollständigen – so u. a. von Gerald Abraham, der ihr eine Zwischenaktmusik aus dem Singspiel *Rosamunde* unterlegte. Eine weitere Theorie behauptet, Selbstkritik hätte Schubert mitten im Scherzo, das er als minderwertig empfand, die Arbeit abbrechen lassen. Maurice J. E. Brown schließlich bringt die Komposition in Zusammenhang mit Schuberts tragischer Erkrankung an Syphilis zu Ende des Jahres 1822, welche ihn aus psychischen Gründen an einer Wiederaufnahme der Kompositionsarbeit gehindert haben soll. Von großer Bedeutung ist auch die Berücksich-tigung von Schuberts individuellem Schaffensprozess, der an Hand der erhaltenen Entwürfe nachvollziehbar ist. Wie in vielen Fällen, so auch in der Sinfonie in h-Moll, umfassen die Klavierskizzen bereits die gesamte geistige Konzeption der späteren Partiturniederschrift, die wesentlich nur eine Reinschrift darstellt. Aus welchen Gründen Schubert auch immer die Komposition im dritten Satz abgebrochen haben mag, hätte es seiner Schaffensweise wider-sprochen, nachträglich Änderungen anzubringen oder die Arbeit neu aufzunehmen.

Auf dem Gebiet der sinfonischen Musik gelang Schubert nie der Durchbruch, wie er ihm seit Beginn der zwanziger Jahre des 19. Jahrhunderts durch seine Liedkompositionen, jene typi-schen Produkte des Biedermeiers, zuteil wurde. Zeitgenössische Konzertprogramme und Zeitungsanzeigen berichten von einer intensiven Pflege Schubert'scher Vokalkompositionen.

X

Auch an Verehrern und Gönnern fehlte es nicht, wie aus der Veranstaltung von so genannten „Schubertiaden", d. h. Hauskonzerten im Freundeskreis, und „Widmungskompositionen" hervorgeht. Zu seinen vielleicht verdienstvollsten Freunden jener Jahre zählte der Wiener Advokat Leopold Sonnleithner (1797–1873), der zusammen mit einigen Kunstfreunden im Frühjahr 1821 die erste Veröffentlichung eines Schubert'schen Werkes („Erlkönig") finanziert hatte. Auf gleiche Weise wurden weitere zwölf Hefte auf eigene Rechnung gestochen und vom Verlag Cappi & Diabelli in Kommission verkauft. Innerhalb der folgenden zwei Jahre wurde Schuberts Name in Wien auch durch Aufführungen zweier Singspiele in führenden Wiener Theater bekannter.

Zum Unterschied von seinem großen Vorbild Beethoven, der schon zu Lebzeiten als Meister der Sinfonik gefeiert wurde, erwarb Schubert seinen ersten Ruhm als Liederkomponist und Meister der Kammerbesetzung. Dennoch gelang ihm auch auf sinfonischem Gebiet mit der h-Moll-Sinfonie erstmals die Loslösung von seinen Vorbildern, indem er ein vollkommen eigenständiges Meisterwerk schuf. Das Jahr der Entstehung 1822 wird auch als Markstein seiner vollen Künstlerreife gewertet.

Im Gegensatz zum konstruktiven Kompositionsprinzip der Wiener Klassiker beruht jenes Schuberts auf der Verwandlung. Das musikalische Geschehen wird hauptsächlich getragen von der Melodie, die schon bei ihrem ersten Erscheinen liedartig in sich geschlossen ist, wie in den beiden Themen des ersten Satzes der h-Moll-Sinfonie (Bläserthema T. 13–20, Streicherthema T. 44–53). Keines dieser Themen liefert jedoch Material für die Durchführung, welche lediglich das Einleitungsthema (T. 1–8) behandelt. Der langsame zweite Satz setzt sich formal aus zwei Teilen zusammen, die beide reprisenartig wiederholt werden.

Seine Vorrangstellung nicht nur innerhalb Schuberts sinfonischem Schaffen verdankt dieses Werk neben den wunderbaren melodischen Einfällen den charakteristischen Klangfarben und der reichen Harmonik, zu deren Mitteln das Modulieren in entfernte Tonarten, der unmittelbare Wechsel von Dur und Moll und die enharmonische Verwechslung gehören.

Um Missverständnisse bezüglich der Nummerierung der letzten Sinfonien Schuberts zu beseitigen, sei erwähnt, dass die lange Zeit gültige unrichtige Zählung der h-Moll-Sinfonie als Nr. 8 und der C-Dur-Sinfonie als Nr. 7 auf Johannes Brahms und die Alte Gesamtausgabe von Schuberts Werken zurückgeführt wird. Um die chronologische Reihenfolge wiederherzustellen, wird vielfach die C-Dur-Sinfonie auch als Nr. 9 gezählt. Seit der revidierten Neuausgabe des „Deutsch-Verzeichnisses" in deutscher Sprache wird die „Unvollendete" chronologisch richtig eingeordnet als Nr. 7.

Teresa Reichenberger

# Symphony No. 7
## 'Unfinished'

Franz Schubert
(1797–1828)
D 759

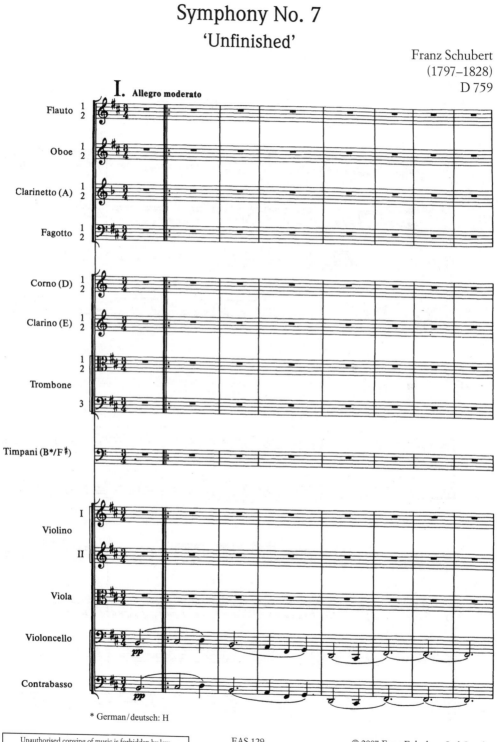

I. Allegro moderato

Flauto 1 2

Oboe 1 2

Clarinetto (A) 1 2

Fagotto 1 2

Corno (D) 1 2

Clarino (E) 1 2

Trombone 1 2 / 3

Timpani (B*/F♯)

Violino I / II

Viola

Violoncello

Contrabasso

* German/deutsch: H

EAS 129

© 2007 Ernst Eulenburg Ltd, London
and Ernst Eulenburg & Co GmbH, Mainz

2

4

6

8

10

EAS 129

12

14

16

18

22

24

28

32

34

38

40

42

44

46

49

EAS 129

50

51

52

54

56

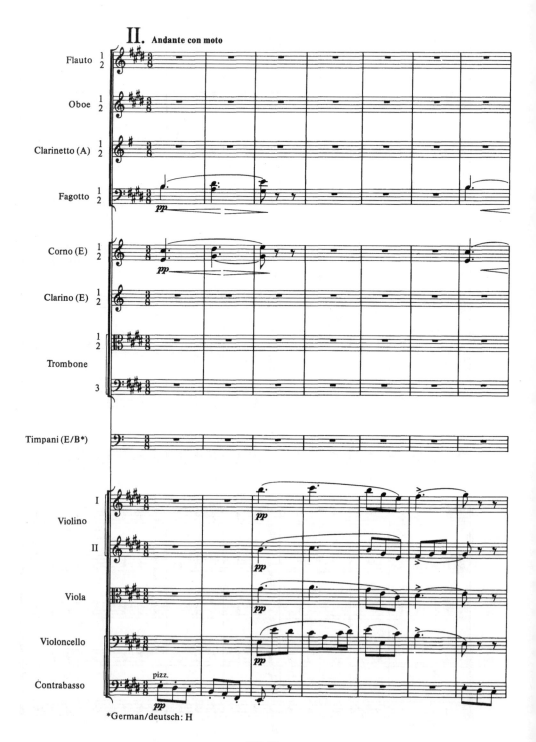

II. Andante con moto

Flauto

Oboe

Clarinetto (A)

Fagotto

Corno (E)

Clarino (E)

Trombone

Timpani (E/B*)

Violino

Viola

Violoncello

Contrabasso

*German/deutsch: H

EAS 129

58

60

66

68

72

74

76

84

88

90

# THE ART OF SCORE-READING

# The first steps

A score contains the entire musical text of a musical work in order that the conductor and everyone who wants to study the piece more thoroughly can see exactly which passages are being played by the orchestra or ensemble. The parts of the individual instruments are arranged in such a way that all notes played at the same time are written one below the other.

Scores help to listen to, understand and interpret musical works. Those who only listen to music are unaware of many important details which, after some practice, become apparent when reading the score while listening to the music. The clear structure of the score helps to easily understand the compositional style and the characteristic features of a piece – this is a prerequisite not only for any analysis but also for the musician's own performance and interpretation.

The simplest method of score-reading is to read an individual part by concentrating on an individual part that can be heard particularly well. The most suitable pieces to begin with are concertos with solo instruments such as Beethoven's Romance in F major for violin and orchestra (example 1) or orchestral songs (with them, one may easily follow the text). Furthermore, in many classical orchestral works, it is quite easy to follow the lead part of the principal violin, or the bass part in baroque compositions for orchestra.

The next step is to try to change from one part to another and vice versa and follow the part that is leading. Little by little, you learn to find distinctive parts you hear in the score as well and follow them in the corresponding staff. This can be very easily tried out with Beethoven's Symphony No. 5 (example 2). To read the score, it is also helpful to count the bars. This technique is rather useful in the case of confusing or complex scores, such as those of contemporary music, and is particularly suitable when you do not want to lag behind in any case. It should be your aim, however, to eventually give up counting the bars and to read the score by first following individual parts and then going over to section-by-section or selective reading (see next page).

Example 1 · from: Romance for violin and orchestra in F major by Beethoven

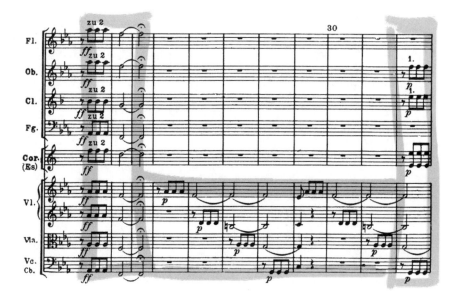

Example 2 · from: Symphony No. 5 C-minor by Beethoven

# Further score-reading techniques

Example 3 · from: Symphony No. 100 G major 'Military' by Haydn

Example 4 · from: Symphony No. 41 C major 'Jupiter' by W. A. Mozart

# Section-by-section reading

This technique is suitable for application in the 'Military' Symphony by Haydn (example 3). In bb. 260-264, the parts are mostly in parallel motion so that it is quite easy to take in the section as a whole. In the strings, the texture is homophonic (i.e. all instruments play the same rhythm), consisting of tone repetitions in the lower parts while there is a little more movement in the part of the first violin. At the same time, the tones of the winds are stationary (i.e. long sustained notes), serving as harmonic filling-in. If need be, they can also be read en bloc.

Such block-like structures often consist of unison figures (= all instruments play the same), such as at the beginning of Mozart's Jupiter Symphony (example 4). Here, the score-reading can first be limited to the strings section which carries the melody alone in bb. 3-4 and contains all important information.

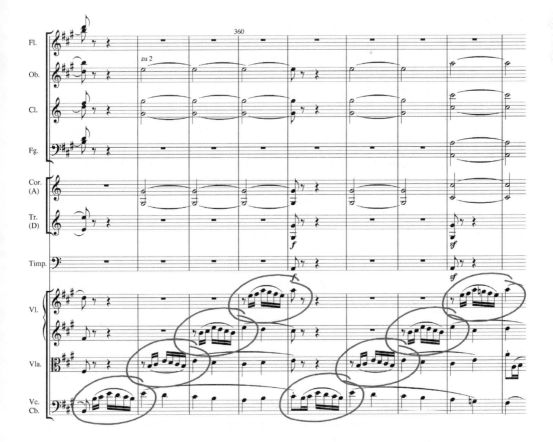

Example 5 · from: Symphony No. 7 A major by Beethoven

# Selektive reading

Using this technique, you concentrate on selected parts (lead parts, conspicuous passages) in the score. In the excerpt from Beethoven's Symphony No. 7 (example 5), it is the semiquaver motif that, originating with the violoncellos and basses and pervading the string parts twice, is particularly well suited. The stationary tones of the winds, consisting only of the note E in various octave positions in bb. 358-363, form the harmonic foundation and play a subordinate role in score-reading. Though they are briefly noticed, it is the strings and especially the conspicuous semiquaver motif pervading the individual parts that are to be followed.

With both score-reading techniques which should be chosen according to the nature of the passage in question, it is not important in the beginning to be able to follow at once all tones and harmonies. What matters more is to recognize and comprehend sequences of movement. Everything else comes with experience.

# Following contrapuntal parts

The present excerpt from Brahms's Requiem (example 6) is polyphonic, i.e. one has to be able to follow several equal parts either alternately (without lagging behind) or simultaneously. But by looking for parallel parts in the score, the notation which, at first glance, seems to be overcrowded soon becomes clearer. For example, Brahms allocates orchestral parts to each choral part. As a consequence, there are many parts written in the score but considerably fewer independent parts actually played. Hence, the large amount of written music can be reduced to a manageable quantity.

The flute, clarinet, first violins and soprano are in parallel motion. Furthermore, the tenor of oboe and viola is supported by a much-expanded, yet parallel part.
The violoncellos and bassoons too are in almost parallel motion.

The low winds and strings as well as the timpani played simultaneously with the polyphonic parts are fill-in parts which consist only of stationary tones (sustained notes). They do not need to be followed upon first reading of the score.

Seen as a whole, this excerpt is most suitable for focussing on the soprano voice as it is coupled with two instruments and, being the highest voice, can be heard very well. In addition, the text is an aid to orientation, making it easier to return from brief trips to other parts.

In fugal sections, score-reading will be easier if the entries of the theme in the score are first looked for and then marked.

Example 6 · from: A German Requiem by Brahms

# The score at a glance

**A** **Bar lines** are solid vertical lines within the instrument sections.

**B** The **bar numbers** are an aid to orientation in the score. Sometimes capital letters, so-called rehearsal letters, are used instead of numbers.

**C** The system of parallel lines on and between which the notes are written is called **staff** (or stave). The instrument abbreviation in front of each line (here, Fl. is for 'flute') indicates to which instrument(s) the line(s) refer(s).

**D** The **barline at the left-hand end** of the staves connects all staves to form the **system**.

**E** In addition to the barline at the left-hand end of the staves, **angular brackets** connect the individual groups of instruments in a score (wind, brass and string instruments). Within these groups, the instruments are arranged according to their pitch, with the highest-pitched instrument mentioned first.
Today, the common order of instrumental parts in the score is as follows, from top to bottom:
· wind instruments
· brass instruments
· percussion instruments
· harp, piano, celesta
· solo instrument(s)
· solo voices
· choir
· string instruments

**F** When there are two systems on a page, they are separated from each other by two parallel **diagonal strokes**.

**G** Instruments the names of which are followed by 'in Bb' or (Bb) are **transposing instruments**. In this case, (Bb) indicates that the notated C is played as Bb, i.e. all tones are played a tone lower than notated. Most of the transposing instruments are easily recognizable in the score thanks to these additions. However, there are also transposing instruments without such indications in the score, such as:
· piccolo flute (in C / an octave higher)
· cor anglais (in F / a fifth lower)
· contrabassoon (in C / an octave lower)
· double bass (in C / an octave lower)

**H** The transposing brass instruments have no general signature but, if need be, accidentals preceding the respective tone.

**I** The viola part is notated in the **alto clef**, the parts of violoncello and bassoon sometimes in the **tenor clef**. Both clefs are easy to read when the player realizes that the clef frames the note C1:
alto clef     tenor clef     treble clef

**J** Any change of key or time is marked by a **double bar**. The alla-breve sign following in this example (¢), like the sign for four-four time (c), is a relic from an old notational practice and stands for two-two time.

100

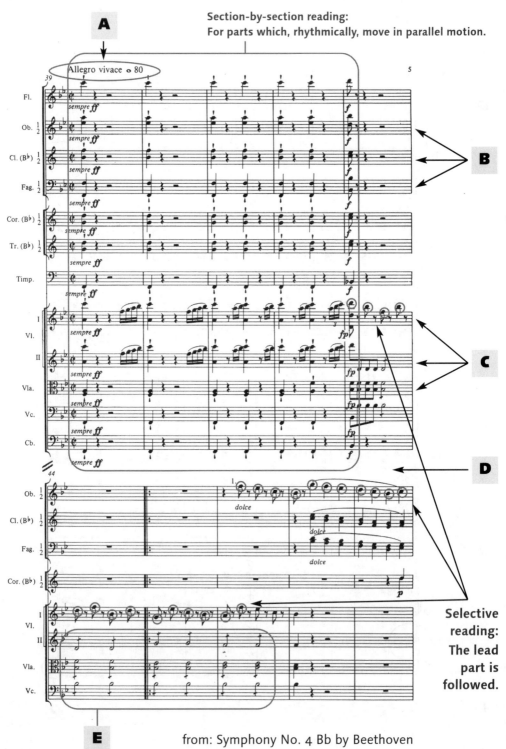

Section-by-section reading:
For parts which, rhythmically, move in parallel motion.

Selective
reading:
The lead
part is
followed.

from: Symphony No. 4 Bb by Beethoven

**A** **Tempo indications** (sometimes in connection with metronome markings) are used by the composer to indicate how fast a piece shall be played.

**B** In the winds, two parts are usually brought together in one line. If they play the same note, the note head either has two stems or 'a2' written above it.

**C** Two-part chords in the staves of the strings are played by one player. If the parts shall be divided, **divisi** (divided) is written in the score. Then, at each desk, one player plays the upper notes and another player the lower notes.

**D** When an instrumental part contains a long rest, as in this flute part for example, its staff is often omitted until the next entry of the instrument, thus saving space. In addition, there are less page-turns, and the playing parts are arranged much clearer.

**E** In order to save space and arrange phrases or groups of notes more clearly, so-called abbreviations are used occasionally. The sign ♩ stands for ♪♪♪♪, with the minim indicating the duration of the repetitions and the stroke crossing the stem indicating the value of the notes to be repeated (1 stroke = quaver, 2 strokes = semiquaver, etc.). Cf. also the viola in b. 43 in which the repeated notes are first written out and then abbreviated.

# Score-Reading with pupils and students!

Order this guideline for score-reading for your class! The leaflet 'The Art of Score-Reading' is available separately or as a set of copies and can be obtained free of charge while stock last.

**Brochure 'The Art of Score-Reading'**
Order No. ETP 9998-99 (free of charge)

# Mozart for the classroom

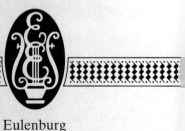

**A picture of life and travel**
Mozart was not only one of the greatest composers, but also one of the best pianists of the 18th century. Like the virtous of today, he spent a large part of his life on concert tours at the leading courts and great cities of his time.

This small brochure depicts a panorama of the musical life in Europe wich formed the background to Mozart's oeuvre. The picture is completed by a short biography and a little insight into his way of composing.

**Brochure 'Mozart. A Picture of Life and Travel'**
Order No. ETP 9991-99 (free of charge)

For further information, see at: www.eulenburg.de

Eulenburg

# DIE KUNST
# DES PARTITURLESENS

# Der erste Einstieg

Eine Partitur enthält den gesamten Notentext eines Musikwerkes, damit der Dirigent und jeder, der sich näher mit dem Stück beschäftigen will, genau nachvollziehen kann, was das Orchester oder das Ensemble spielt. Dabei sind die Instrumente so angeordnet, dass alle Noten, die zur gleichen Zeit erklingen, genau untereinander stehen. Partituren helfen beim Hören, Begreifen und Interpretieren von Musikliteratur. Wer nur zuhört, erkennt viele kostbare Kleinigkeiten nicht, die beim Mitlesen nach ein wenig Übung regelrecht sichtbar werden. Der Kompositionsstil und die Charakteristik eines Werkes lassen sich mit der übersichtlichen Partitur schnell begreifen – das ist nicht nur Grundvoraussetzung für jede Analyse, sondern auch für das eigene Spiel.

Die einfachste Methode beim Partiturlesen ist das Verfolgen einer Einzelstimme. Bei diesem Verfahren konzentriert man sich auf eine einzelne Stimme, die besonders gut zu hören ist. Zum Einstieg eignen sich dabei besonders gut Konzerte mit Soloinstrumenten wie die Romanze in F-Dur für Violine und Orchester von Beethoven (Beispiel 1) oder Orchesterlieder (bei letzteren kann man sich leicht am Text orientieren). Weiterhin kann man bei vielen klassischen Orchesterwerken die führende Stimme der ersten Violine gut verfolgen, sowie bei barocken Kompositionen für Orchester die Bass-Stimme.

In einem nächsten Schritt kann man versuchen, zwischen den Stimmen zu wechseln und jeweils die Stimme zu verfolgen, die gerade führend ist. Nach und nach lernt man dabei markante Stimmen, die man hört, auch in der Partitur zu finden und im entsprechenden Notensystem zu verfolgen. Besonders anschaulich kann man das mittels Beethovens 5. Symphonie erproben (Beispiel 2).
Eine weitere Hilfe beim Lesen der Partitur kann auch das Mitzählen der Takte sein. Dieses Verfahren hilft bei unübersichtlichen oder komplexen Partituren wie etwa zeitgenössischer Musik und eignet sich besonders, wenn man den Anschluss auf keinen Fall verlieren möchte. Ziel sollte es jedoch sein, das Mitzählen der Takte gänzlich zu verlassen und die Partitur zunächst anhand einzelner Stimmen und dann im Wechsel von blockweisem bzw. selektivem Lesen zu verfolgen (siehe nächste Seite).

Beispiel 1 · aus: Romanze für Violine und Orchester F-Dur von Beethoven

Beispiel 2 · aus: Symphonie Nr. 5 c-moll von Beethoven

# Weitere Methoden des Partiturlesens

Beispiel 3 · aus: Symphonie Nr. 100 G-Dur „Militär" von Haydn

Beispiel 4 · aus: Symphonie Nr. 41 C-Dur „Jupiter" von W. A. Mozart

# Blockweises Lesen

Diese Methode bietet sich in der Militär-Symphonie von Haydn an (Beispiel 3). In den T. 260-264 sind die Stimmen weitgehend parallel geführt, so dass man sie gut im Ganzen überblicken kann. In den Streichern haben wir einen homophonen Satz (d.h. alle Stimmen spielen den gleichen Rhythmus), der in den unteren Stimmen aus Tonwiederholungen besteht, während die erste Violine etwas bewegter ist. Gleichzeitig erklingen in den Bläserstimmen Liegetöne (d.h. lang ausgehaltene Töne), die als harmonischer Füllstoff dienen. Sie können bei Bedarf auch im Block gelesen werden.
Oft bestehen solche blockhaften Gebilde auch aus unisono-Figuren (= alle Stimmen spielen dasselbe), wie z.B. am Beginn der Jupiter-Symphonie von Mozart (Beispiel 4). Hier kann man sich beim Lesen zunächst nur auf den Streicherblock beschränken, der in den T. 3-4 alleine die Melodie weiterführt und bereits alle wichtigen Informationen enthält.

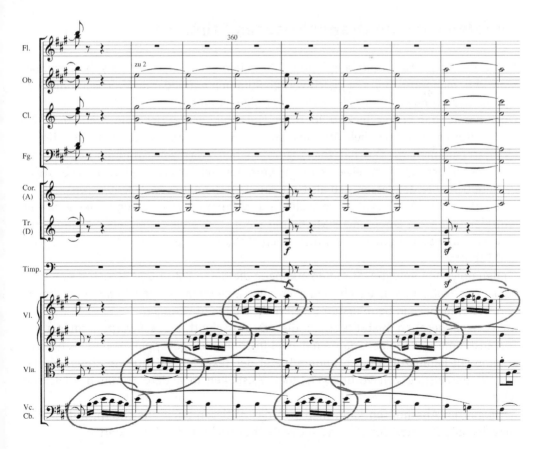

Beispiel 5 · aus: Symphonie Nr. 7 A-Dur von Beethoven

# Selektives Lesen

Bei dieser Methode orientiert man sich anhand ausgewählter Stimmen (führende Stimmen, auffällige Stellen) in der Partitur. Im Ausschnitt aus Beethovens 7. Symphonie (Beispiel 5) ist hierzu das Sechzehntelmotiv geeignet, das zweimal von den Celli und Bässen ausgehend durch die Streicherstimmen wandert. Die Liegetöne der Bläser, die in den T. 358-363 sogar nur aus dem Ton e in unterschiedlichen Oktavlagen bestehen, bilden die harmonische Grundierung und spielen beim Lesen der Partitur eine untergeordnete Rolle. Man nimmt sie kurz wahr, verfolgt jedoch die Streicher und dort insbesondere das auffällige Sechzehntelmotiv in seiner Wanderung durch die einzelnen Stimmen.

Bei beiden Leseformen, zwischen denen man übrigens je nach Beschaffenheit der Stelle wechseln sollte, kommt es am Anfang nicht darauf an, sofort alle Töne und Harmonien verfolgen zu können. Viel wichtiger ist es, Bewegungsabläufe zu erkennen und nachzuvollziehen. Alles Weitere kommt mit der Erfahrung.

# Verfolgen von kontrapunktischen Stimmen

Der vorliegende Ausschnitt aus Brahms' Requiem (Beispiel 6) ist polyphon komponiert, d.h. man muss mehrere gleichwertige Stimmen entweder im Wechsel (ohne den Anschluss zu verlieren) oder gleichzeitig verfolgen können.

Doch das auf den ersten Blick so übervolle Notenbild lichtet sich bald, wenn man sich die Partitur näher auf parallele Stimmen ansieht. Brahms ordnet z.B. jeder Chorstimme Orchesterstimmen zu. Das hat zur Folge, dass hier zwar viele Stimmen notiert sind, aber wesentlich weniger eigenständige Stimmen tatsächlich erklingen. Die vielen geschriebenen Noten lassen sich also auf ein überschaubares Maß reduzieren.

So werden Flöte, Klarinette, erste Violinen und Sopran parallel geführt. Des Weiteren wird der Tenor von Oboe und Bratsche mit einer stark erweiterten, aber dennoch parallel verlaufenden Stimme unterstützt. Ebenfalls fast ganz parallel verlaufen Violoncelli und Fagotte.

Zu den polyphon gefügten Stimmen erklingen die tiefen Bläser und Streicher sowie die Pauke mit Füllstimmen, welche lediglich aus Liegetönen (ausgehaltene Töne) bestehen. Sie braucht man beim ersten Lesen nicht weiter zu verfolgen.

Im Ganzen gesehen bietet sich in diesem Ausschnitt an, schwerpunktmäßig die Sopranstimme zu verfolgen, da sie mit zwei Instrumenten gekoppelt ist und als höchste Stimme gut herauszuhören ist. Zudem bietet der Text eine Orientierungshilfe, so dass der Wiedereinstieg von vorübergehenden Ausflügen in andere Stimmen erleichtert wird.

Bei fugierten Abschnitten kann man sich das Mitlesen auch erleichtern, indem man zunächst alle Einsätze des Themas in der Partitur sucht und sich markiert.

Beispiel 6 · aus: Ein deutsches Requiem von Brahms

# Die Partitur im Überblick

**A** **Taktstriche** sind innerhalb der Instrumentengruppen durchgezogen.

**B** Die **Taktzahlen** erleichtern die Orientierung in der Partitur. Manchmal dienen hierzu auch Großbuchstaben, sog. Studierbuchstaben.

**C** Eine einzelne Zeile der Partitur nennt man **Notensystem**. Für welche(s) Instrument(e) sie steht, zeigt der **Instrumentenvorsatz** an (hier Fl. für Flöte).

**D** Der **Kopfstrich** verbindet alle Notensysteme miteinander zu einer **Akkolade**.

**E** Zusätzlich zum Kopfstrich fassen **gerade Klammern** die einzelnen Instrumentengruppen (Holz-, Blech- und Streichinstrumente) zusammen. Innerhalb dieser Gruppen sind die Instrumente nach Tonlage geordnet, wobei das höchste an oberster Stelle steht.
Die heute übliche Partituranordnung lautet von oben nach unten:
· Holzblasinstrumente
· Blechblasinstrumente
· Schlaginstrumente
· Harfe, Klavier, Celesta
· Soloinstrument(e)
· Solostimmen
· Chor
· Streichinstrumente

**F** Stehen zwei Akkoladen auf einer Seite, werden sie durch zwei **Schrägstriche** voneinander abgetrennt.

**G** Steht hinter dem Instrumentennamen z.B. „in B" oder (B), handelt es sich um ein **transponierendes Instrument**. In diesem Fall deutet das (B) an, dass das notierte C als B erklingt, also alle Noten einen Ton tiefer erklingen als sie notiert sind. Die meisten transponierenden Instrumente sind in der Partitur durch diese Zusätze leicht zu erkennen. Es gibt aber auch transponierende Instrumente ohne eine entsprechende Angabe in der Partitur, wie z.B.:
Piccoloflöte (in c/eine Oktave höher)
Englischhorn (in f/eine Quinte tiefer)
Kontrafagott (in c/eine Oktave tiefer)
Kontrabass (in c/eine Oktave tiefer)

**H** Die transponierenden Blechblasinstrumente haben keine Generalvorzeichen, sondern bei Bedarf Versetzungszeichen, die direkt vor der jeweiligen Note stehen.

**I** Die Viola oder Bratsche wird im **Alt- bzw. Bratschenschlüssel** notiert, die Stimmen des Violoncellos und Fagotts manchmal im **Tenorschlüssel**. Beide Schlüssel sind leicht zu lesen, wenn man sich klarmacht, dass der Schlüssel den Ton c1 umrahmt, also:
Alt-          Tenor-          Violinschlüssel

**J** Vor einem Wechsel der Ton- oder Taktart steht immer ein **Doppelstrich**. Das hier folgende Alla-Breve-Zeichen (¢) ist ebenso wie das Zeichen für den 4/4-Takt (c) ein Relikt aus einer älteren Notationspraxis und steht für den 2/2-Takt.

111

112

Blockweises Lesen:
Bei rhythmisch parallelgeführten Stimmen.

Selektives
Lesen:
Man verfolgt
die führende
Stimme.

aus: Symphonie Nr. 4 B-Dur von Beethoven

**A** Durch die **Tempoangabe** (manchmal mit einer Metronomzahl verbunden) gibt der Komponist an, wie schnell ein Stück gespielt werden soll.

**B** Bei den Bläsern werden in der Regel zwei Stimmen in einer Notenzeile zusammengefasst. Spielen sie den gleichen Ton, erhält der Notenkopf zwei Hälse oder es steht a2 darüber.

**C** Zweistimmige Akkorde in den Notensystemen der Streicher werden von einem Spieler gespielt. Will man die Stimmen aufteilen, schreibt man **divisi** (geteilt). Dann spielt an jedem Pult ein Spieler die oberen und ein Spieler die unteren Noten.

**D** Hat eine Stimme, wie hier die Flöte, längere Zeit Pause, wird ihr Notensystem oft bis zum erneuten Einsatz der Stimme weggelassen. So wird Platz gespart, man muß weniger blättern und die erklingenden Stimmen sind übersichtlicher angeordnet.

**E** Um Platz zu sparen und Tonfolgen übersichtlicher zu gestalten, verwendet man gelegentlich sogenannte **Abbreviaturen (Faulenzer)**. Das hier verwendete Zeichen ♩ steht für ♪♪♪♪, wobei die Halbe Note die Dauer der Wiederholungen anzeigt und der Strich durch den Notenhals den Wert der zu wiederholenden Noten (1 Strich = Achtel, 2 = Sechzehntel usw.). Vgl. auch die Viola in T. 43, in der zunächst die Repetitionen ausgeschrieben und dann abgekürzt sind.

# Partiturlesen im Klassensatz

Diese kurze Einführung können Sie als kostenloses Faltblatt bestellen – gern auch im Klassensatz!
**Faltblatt "Die Kunst des Partiturlesens"**
Bestellnummer: ETP 9999-99 (kostenlos)

Die passende Ergänzung für Klassen- und Unterrichtsräume:
**Plakat A2 "Die Partitur im Überblick"**
Bestellnummer ETP 9950-99 (kostenlos)

# Mozart im Klassensatz

**Ein Lebens- und Reisebild**
Mozart war nicht nur einer der größten Komponisten, sondern auch einer der besten Pianisten des 18. Jahrhunderts. Wie heutige Virtuosen verbrachte er große Teile seines Lebens auf Konzertreisen zwischen den führenden Höfen und großen Städten seiner Zeit. Diese kleine Broschüre entfaltet ein Panorama des europäischen Musiklebens, das den Hintergrund für Mozarts Schaffen bildete. Eine Kurzbiographie und ein kleiner Einblick in seine Schreibweise runden das Bild ab.
**Faltblatt "Mozart. Ein Lebens- und Reisebild"**
Bestellnummer ETP 9990-99 (kostenlos)

Weitere Informationen unter www.eulenburg.de

Eulenburg